STORY
BRIAN FINKELSTEIN
BILL JEMAS
MICHAEL COAST

SCRIPT
BRIAN FINKELSTEIN

LAYOUTS
JULIAN ROWE

PENCILS
JOSEPH COOPER

COLORS
LIEZL BUENAVENTURA
THE HORIES

COVER
APPLE QINGYANG ZHANG

LETTERS
RICHARD BROOKS

EDITOR
RICHARD BROOKS

DOUBLE TAKE

RICHARD BROOKS | PRODUCTION ASSISTANT

MICHAEL COAST | STORY EDITOR

CLAIRE DRANGINIS | PRODUCTION COORDINATOR

CAROLINE FLANAGAN | PRODUCTION ASSISTANT

ALLISON GADSDEN | EDITORIAL INTERN

WILLIAM GRAVES | DIGITAL PRODUCTION ARTIST

CHARLOTTE GREENBAUM | EDITORIAL ASSISTANT

YOUNG HELLER | STORYBOARD ILLUSTRATOR

BILL JEMAS | GENERAL MANAGER

ELYSIA LIANG | EDITORIAL ASSISTANT

ROBERT MEYERS | MANAGING EDITOR

JULIAN ROWE | STORYBOARD ILLUSTRATOR

LILLIAN TAN | BUSINESS MANAGER

GABE YOCUM | SALES & MARKETING COORDINATOR

...ab #1. September 2015. Published by Double Take, LLC, a subsidiary of Take-Two Interactive Software, Inc. Office of publication: 38 W. ...9 Street, 2nd Floor, New York, NY 10018. ©2015 Take-Two Interactive Software, Inc. All Rights Reserved. Printed in Canada.

PRIME TIME GUIDE

APRIL 24TH–30TH, 1966

Day	Time	ABC	CBS	NBC	WJAC-TV DuBOIS
SUNDAY	6:30	Local	Local	Bell Telephone Hour/NBC News Specials	Walter Kronkite
	7:00	Voyage to the Bottom of the Sea	Lassie		Rifleman
	7:30		It's About Time	Walt Disney's Wonderful World of Color	To Tell the Truth
	8:00	The FBI	Ed Sullivan Show		I've Got a Secret
	8:30			Hey Landlord!	Lucy Show
	9:00	The Sunday Night Movie	Garry Moore Show	Bonanza	Andy Griffith Show
	9:30				Hazel
	10:00		Candid Camera	Andy Williams Show	Strollin' 20's
	10:30		What's My Line?		
MONDAY	7:30	Iron Horse	Gilligan's Island	The Monkees	Gunsmoke
	8:00		Run, Buddy, Run	I Dream of Jeannie	Pirate Fever 66
	8:30	The Rat Patrol	The Lucy Show	Roger Miller Show	Lucy Show
	9:00	The Felony Squad	Andy Griffith Show	The Road West	Andy Griffith Show
	9:30	Peyton Place	Family Affair		Family Affair
	10:00	The Big Valley	Jess Arthur Show	Run For Your Life	Run For Your Life
	10:30		I've Got a Secret		
TUESDAY	7:30	Combat!	Daktari	The Girl From U.N.C.L.E.	12 O'Clock High
	8:00				
	8:30	The Rounders	Red Skelton Hour	Occasional Wife	Legend of Jesse James
	9:00	The Pruitts of Southampton			Shenandoah
	9:30	Love on a Rooftop	Petticoat Junction	Tuesday Night at the Movies	Peyton Place
	10:00	The Fugitive	CBS News Special		Ben Casey
	10:30				
WEDNESDAY	7:30	Batman	Lost In Space	The Virginian	Hullabaloo
	8:00	The Monroes			John Forsythe Show
	8:30		The Beverly Hillbillies		Dr. Kildare
	9:00	The Man Who Never Was	Green Acres	Bob Hope Show and Specials	Andy Williams Show
	9:30	Peyton Place	Gomer Pyle, USMC		
	10:00	ABC Stage 67	Danny Kaye Show	I Spy	Run For Your Life
	10:30				
THURSDAY	7:30	Batman	Jericho	Daniel Boone	Batman
	8:00	F Troop			Hullabaloo
	8:30	Tammy Grimes Show	My Three Sons	Star Trek	Lucy Show
	9:00	Bewitched			Family Affair
	9:30	That Girl	The CBS Thursday Night Movies	The Hero	My Three Sons
	10:00	Hawk		Dean Martin Show	Big Valley
	10:30				
FRIDAY	7:30	The Green Hornet	The Wild, Wild West	Tarzan	World Today
	8:00	The Time Tunnel			12 O'Clock High
	8:30		Hogan's Heroes	The Man from U.N.C.L.E.	Hazel
	9:00	Milton Barie Show			Peyton Place
	9:30		The CBS Friday Night Movies	T.H.E. Cat	Lucy Show
	10:00	12 O'Clock High		Laredo	Merv Griffin Show
	10:30				
SATURDAY	7:30	Shane	Jackie Gleeson Show	Flipper	Pitt at Johnstown Quiz
	8:00			Please Don't Eat the Daisies	John Forsythe Show
	8:30	The Lawrence Welk Show	Pistols 'N' Petticoats	Get Smart	Dr. Kildare
	9:00		Mission: Impossible		Andy Williams Show
	9:30	The Hollywood Palace		Saturday Night at the Movies	
	10:00		Gunsmoke		Run for Your Life
	10:30	ABC Scope			

The bodies should be disposed of at once, preferably by cremation.

It's only a matter of minutes, before they become reactivated.

Minutes? That doesn't give people time to make arrangements...

No, you're right. It doesn't give them time to make funeral arrangements.

The bodies must be carried to the street and burned. They must be burned immediately.

Soak them with gasoline and burn them.

The bereaved will have to forgo the dubious comforts that a funeral service will give.

They're just dead flesh. And dangerous.

We should give this guy his own show!

ON AIR

It's like having Vincent Price in the studio!

Between you and me, how is this going to play out?

Not enough data to support a fair conclusion.

But it is fair to say that massive death is imminent.

This guy is rich. We gotta get more of him.

Are you kidding me? He's like the fifth horseman of the apocalypse.

Dr. Grimes we would like you to stay and do a more comprehensive interview.

No.

But by being here, your insight can save lives.

I won't be any trouble. You'll hardly even notice I'm there.

That guy is rich!

He's horrifying.

Sure he's horrifying, but it's ratings gold!

Maybe we'll get lucky and he'll kill some puppies.

Can you survive the zombie apocalypse?

Yes? You probably think you can.

There is only one way to find out.

Play the **Dead Reign® RPG**. The core rule book, a few players, some dice and an active imagination are all you need to start playing. Rules are easy. Character creation is fast and fun. Combat, quick and deadly. Survival? Harder than you may think.

- **7 different types of zombies. Zombie combat and survival tips.**
- **6 Apocalyptic Character Classes and Ordinary People.**
- **101 Random Scenarios, Encounters, Settings and places of note.**
- **100 Random Corpse Searches, other tables, weapons & vehicles.**
- **Death Cults, their Priests, power over zombies and goals.**
- **Quick Roll Character Creation tables (10 minutes).**
- **5 sourcebooks provide more types of zombies, survival tips, new dangers and adventure.**
- **The Dead Reign™ core rule book is 224 pages – Cat. No. 230. A complete role-playing game book.**

Discover the Palladium Books® RPG Megaverse®

Fun to read. A blast to play. The Palladium role-playing rule system is the same in every game. This means once readers become familiar with one game, they can play them *ALL*.

Better yet, you can link and combine several game worlds to create epic, multi-dimensional adventures on a cosmic scale!

What's that? You've never seen a role-playing game? The role-playing core rule book contains all the rules and data you need to create characters and get you started. Each game or supplement is a magazine size soft-bound or hardcover book, 48-352 pages, and jam-packed with great art, heroes, villains, adventure and tons of ideas. **Dead Reign®** and **Robotech®** are excellent for those of you new to pen and paper RPGs.

Rifts® is the Earth of the future, but a transformed and alien Earth where magic and technology coexist and realities from countless dimensions collide. Alien predators and supernatural monsters prey upon the human survivors and threaten to conquer the world.

Players can be any number of aliens, mutants, warriors, cyborgs, robots and wizards. Lines of magic crisscross the Earth, giving life to dragons, godlings and supernatural horrors. They also lead to dimensional gateways called "Rifts" that link the Earth to the infinite Megaverse®. In **Rifts®** anything is possible.

Unleash your imagination! Drop by our website to learn more about our games or make purchases from our online store. Also available in comic book and game stores everywhere.

www.palladiumbooks.com

I tried calling her but got no answer.

I want to come there.

I don't know. Your dad is very busy. He--

The dead?! Back to life?! What about Carol?!

I DON'T CARE! COME GET ME!

Okay. Okay. I will come get you.

We can pick up Carol on the way.

SID MEIER'S CIVILIZATION
BEYOND EARTH

WWW.CIVILIZATION.COM

FIRAXIS
GAMES

2K

Any update in DC?

Off the record.

The Assistant Director says radiation levels are rising.

How's that possible? They blew up the probe two days ago.

I'll ask. Stay tuned.

Reports are in from Washington that radiation levels are rising.

...advised to seek out those rescue stations as soon as possible. There are now reports in from Washington that radiation levels continue to rise.

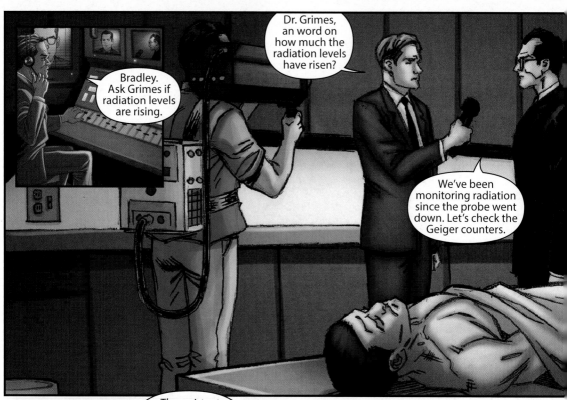

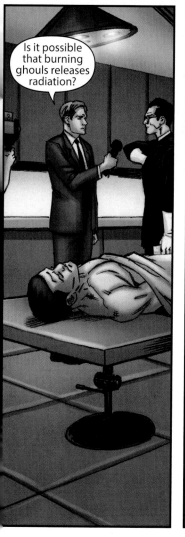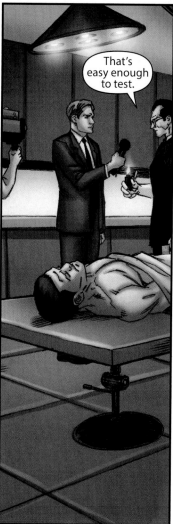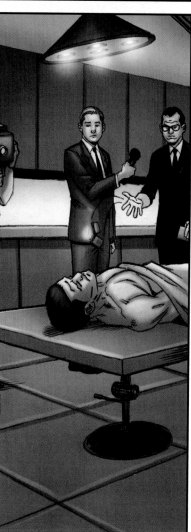

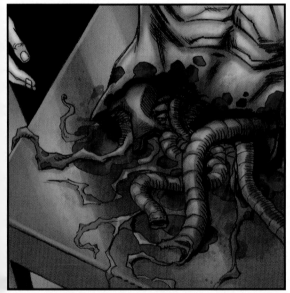

Interesting.

I smell a Pulitzer.

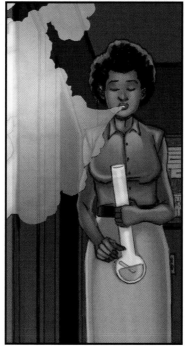

THANK YOU
FOR YOUR CONTRIBUTIONS, COLLABORATION, AND SUPPORT.

Strauss Zelnick
Hao Zheng
Dwight Zimmerman
Billy Yocum
Butch & Susan Yocum
Jerry Wang
Peter Welch
Heather Werber
Adam Wexler
Mitchell Wojcik
Michael Worosz
Bob Wulff
Teodora Varga
Jean Vargas
John Taddeo
David & Jean Tan
Rebecca Tan
Jamie Tanner
Jude Terror
Peter Thomatos
Zac Thompson
April Salazar
Darren Sanchez
Sam Saxton
Cassandra Schaffa
Gareb Shamus
Klaus Shmidheiser
Cori Silberman
Jeffrey Simons
Karl Slatoff
Mat Smart
Catherine Smyka
Jay Spence
Kingston Stafford
Lili Stiefel
Sage Stossel
Ethan Rasiel
Mike Rivera

John Roberts
John Robinson
Hans Rodionoff
Mike Rosenzweig
Sharon & Blake Rowe
Emmanuel Ogwang
Dino Pai
Ron Perazza
Rock Persaud
Fred Pierce
Amanda Proscia
Qui Nguyen
Nicole Nicoletti
Jai Nitz
Ralph Macchio
Max MacDonald
Brian David Marshall
Mike Martucci
Michael Meyers
Peter Milligan
Jane Milrod
Tom Mitchell
Randy Monkarsh
Michaela Murphy
Tony Lee
Ken Levine
Josh Leuze
Alan Lewis
Ping Liang
Stephen Liang
Gui Karyo
Jordan Katz
Maria Jagodka
Rose & Bill Jemas
Orissa Jenkins
Rich Johnston
Dan Jolly
Justin Jordan

Alex Hamby
Harry Haramis
Daniel Heacox
Daniel & Hyo Nam Heller
Krystof & Krystal Heller
Young Ai Heller
Peter Herrmann
Keith Hilber
Matt Hoverman
Darren Hutchinson
Daniel Gallina
Court Gebeau
Hayley Geftman-Gold
Greg Gibson
Flinn Gillan
David Macho Gómez
Sarah Gordon
Andrew Granik
Bobby Graves
Robert Graves
Robin Murphy Graves
Kathryn Greenbaum
John Greenbaum
John Falco
Adam Fenton
Christopher Fiumano
Claire Flanagan
Fiona Flanagan
Nancy & Tim Flanagan
Teresa Focarille
Drew Ford
Atom Freeman
Chris Eaton
Otto Eckstein
Carter Edwards
Daniel Einzig
Howard Emanuel
Vonnetta Ewing

Kathleen Davis
Shawn DeLoache
Kimberly Devaney
Gavin Dillinger
Mike Dolce
Stan & Janet Dranginis
Lucas Duimstra
Christian Cafiero
Jason Calvert
Peter Carbonaro
Chris Casazza
Skye Chalmers
Ben Chamberlain
Larry Charlip
Muhammad Chaudhry
Stephanie Chu
Brian Clevinger
Bill & Mary Coast
David Cox
Maria Barreras
Peter Begler
Ian Berry
Cheryl & Larry Bishop
Ralph Blaser
Siobhan Boes
Tommy Bolduc
Phil Boyle
Maya Bronfman
Juliette Brooks
Gahl Buslov
Tony Buttino
Jared Atchison
Chris Arrant
Christle Arriola
Tisha Ayala
Ellen Dranginis
Antoine Boisvert
KB Breiseth

All of us here, at Double Take admire and respect the creators, cast and crew, of the 1968 film *Night of the Living Dead.* While no one affiliated with the film has been involved in the creation of these stories, their wonderful work inspired us.

To be continued...

SLAB #2
FRESH FLESH

NEXT ISSUE

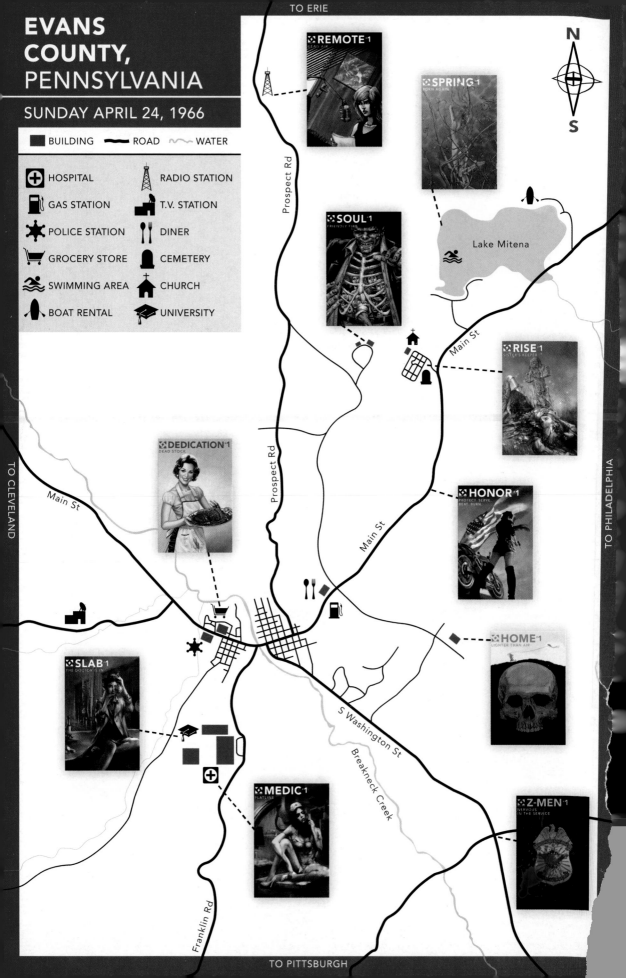